THE
Big Brown Bear

By GEORGES DUPLAIX
Illustrated by GUSTAF TENGGREN

A GOLDEN BOOK • NEW YORK
Western Publishing Company, Inc., Racine, Wisconsin 53404

Once there was a big brown bear who lived with his wife inside a cave.

"Please, dear," his wife said to him one day, "run down to the brook and catch some fish for dinner.

"But don't go near the beehive in the old dead tree," she warned. "Remember what those bees did to you last time."

The big brown bear walked slowly toward
the brook. Before he knew it, though, he was
at the old dead tree!

He pushed his paw right into the hive. Inside, the busy bees were making wax and honey. The big brown bear grabbed a piece of sweet, chewy honeycomb.

The minute the bees saw that great big
paw wrecking their home and stealing their
precious honey, they rushed out.

The big brown bear ran away so fast that he left the bees far behind him.

But alas! He caught his foot in the root of a tree and tumbled over and over and rolled down the hill into a thorn bush.

Swarming after him in a big cloud, the
bees were ready to zoom down on his head.
So the poor bear had to act fast.

Pulling and kicking and tugging, he tore himself loose at last, leaving a great deal of his fur in the bush.

He ran toward the brook, jumped into the water, and hid there with only his nose showing. Suddenly the bees spotted him and swooped down smack on his nose.

"Ouch! Ouch!" he cried, and ran out of the brook into a grassy field.

He hid in the tall grass where the bees could not see him. His nose was sore and getting bigger and bigger.

And he was supposed to catch some fish
for dinner!

Back he went to the brook and quickly he caught a trout. Then he ran toward home, looking over his shoulder fearfully.

He was so happy to be home that he gave his wife a great big bear hug and kissed her on both ears. His wife was quite surprised by such a greeting and guessed right away that he had done something wrong.

And as soon as she saw his nose, she knew what he had done.

"Oh, dear!" she cried. "Why did you go near those bees?"

The big brown bear had no excuse. He promised that he would never, never go near the old dead tree again.

His wife put a bandage on his nose. She gave him the biggest piece of trout.

But way deep inside, he wished he had some of that nice honey for dessert.